GRADE 06

PIANO

Pieces & Exercises for
Trinity College London
Exams 2018–2020

Published by
Trinity College London Press
trinitycollege.com

Registered in England
Company no. 09726123

Copyright © 2017 Trinity College London Press
First impression, June 2017

Printed in England by Halstan & Co Ltd., Amersham, Bucks

Coranto

No. 218 from *Fitzwilliam Virginal Book*

William Byrd
(1540-1623)

Prelude in D minor

BWV 935

Johann Sebastian Bach
(1685-1750)

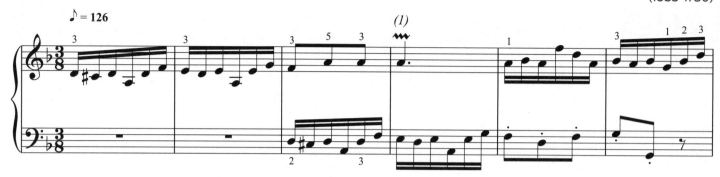

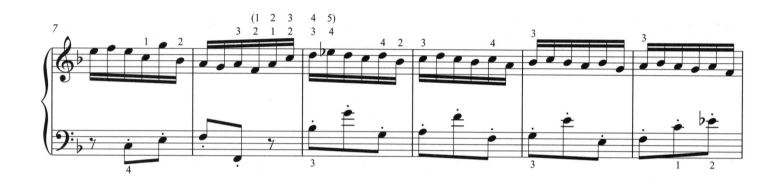

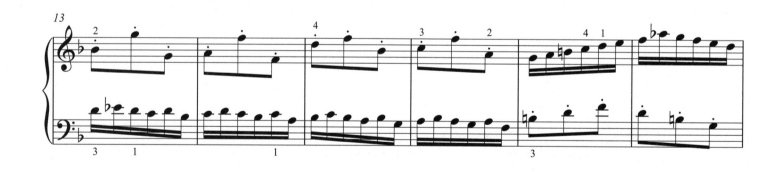

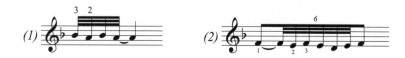

5

Sonatina in E flat

Georg Anton Benda
(1722-1795)

9

Giga in A minor

Richard Jones
(d. 1744)

Arabesque

op. 6 no. 4

Genary Karganov
(1858-1890)

Moderato con espressione (e rubato) ♩ = 96

Progression I

Manfred Schmitz
(1939-2014)

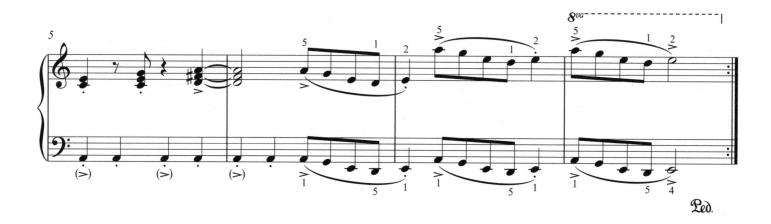

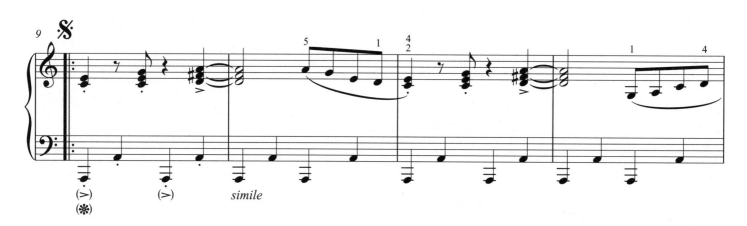

to Coda last time

D. S. al Coda

Coda

[Blank page to facilitate page turns]

Weaving a Spell

Robert Ramskill
(b. 1950)

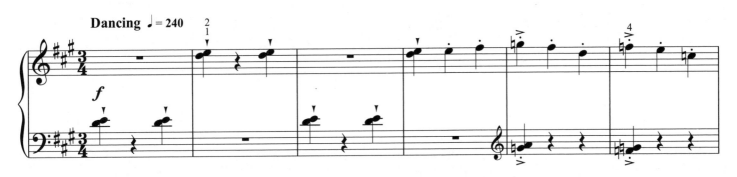

To Coda ⊕
2nd time

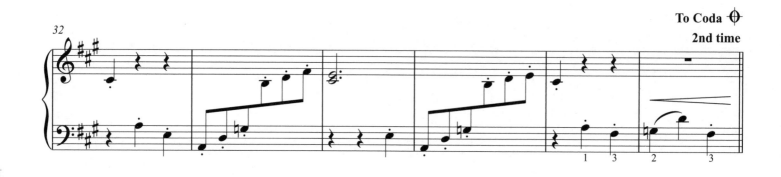

D.S. al Coda

CODA

Mazurka

Nathalie Béra-Tagrine
(b. 1960)

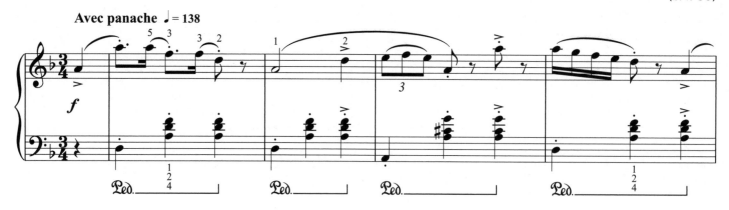

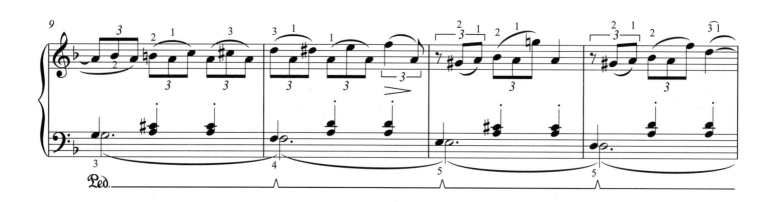

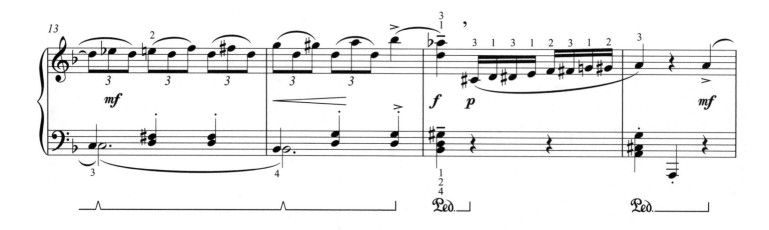

In Dreams

from The Lord of the Rings: The Fellowship of the Ring

Arr. Podgornov

Howard Shore / Fran Walsh
(b. 1946 / b. 1959)

Exercises

1a. Nouvelle Gymnopédie – tone, balance and voicing

F + C
white

1b. Romantic Gesture – tone, balance and voicing

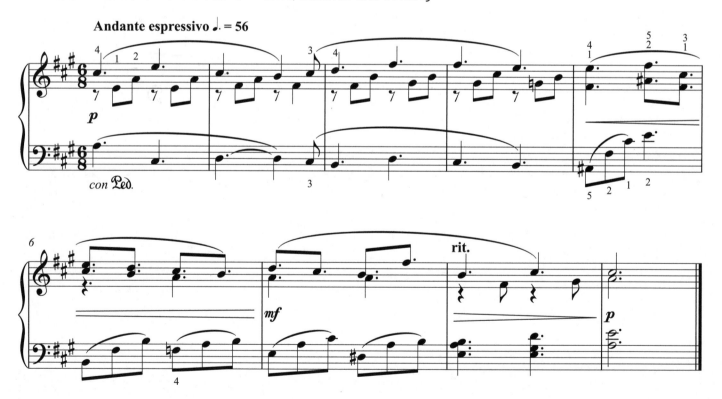

2a. Spinal Chords – co-ordination

2b. Three Against Two Ain't Fair! – co-ordination

3a. Catch Me If You Can! – finger & wrist strength and flexibility

3b. The Fugitive – finger & wrist strength and flexibility